# Table of Contents

D1164325

# I. Introduction

The role of the Patient Advocate is to support patient rights and to ensure the safety and satisfaction of the patient. Throughout its more than 40 year history, the Patient Advocacy Community (PAC) of the Beryl Institute, formerly known as the Society for Healthcare Consumer Advocacy (SHCA), has worked on behalf of patients and organizations to improve the patient care experience and protect patients' rights.

One need not go far to find examples in the news, or in our personal lives, that demonstrate the importance of the patient advocacy role. As our healthcare delivery system grows more complex, and as more people seek healthcare services, it is clear that we, as Patient Advocates, have an important contribution to make in the lives of our patients and their families. No matter what our title—Patient Advocate, Representative, Navigator, or Liaison—we are vital contributors to supporting patients and families as they navigate the healthcare system.

The contents of this guide are organized to assist Patient Advocates and others in healthcare organizations to anticipate, meet, and even exceed the expectations of patients receiving care. The PAC of the Beryl Institute has created it as a quick reference to the Centers for Medicare and Medicaid Services (CMS) regulations regarding the complaint and grievance management process. The guide includes some history of the creation and evolution of the CMS regulations[1], the intent of the guidelines, and examples of policies to assist you in managing grievances and complaints more effectively in your organization. At the back of the guide you will find references to the regulations, the Conditions of Participation, The Joint Commission standards and the ethical standards to which professional patient advocates commit. Lastly, The Beryl Institute's useful resources are included as well[2].

Our hope is that you will keep this guide handy and find it a useful reference.

# A Patient-Centered Approach to Handling Complaints and Grievances

## SECOND EDITION

**2015 PAC Publications Members:**
Linda Reiser, Chair, 2015 The Beryl Institute
PAC Publications Committee, 2012 SHCA
Publications Committee
Eve DeVaro
Mary Ellen Namoff
Lara Klick

**2012 Contributors:**
Linda Taloney
Mary Willis
Marianne Sailus
Ellen Martin
Jessica Chambers

**Original Contributors:**
Jerri Scarzella
Chastity Johnson
Roseanna Ryan
Linda Taloney
Rita Erlandson
Sonia Martinez
Debra Olsen
Mary Willis

The Beryl Institute
3600 Harwood Road, Suite A
Bedford, TX 76021
www.theberylinstitute.org

ISBN 978-0-9903728-2-0
Printed in the United States of America

# II. Managing the Patient Grievance and Complaint Process

Healthcare organizations are driven to manage the complaint and grievance process for three fundamental reasons:

- They are focused on delivering patient-centered care
- It's the right thing to do from a quality perspective
- It's a regulatory obligation

## Patient Management Principles

It is imperative that all staff members have good communication skills when dealing with patients and their representatives. This is especially true for those dealing with patient complaints and grievances.

Five essential principles should guide your approach to ensure that the person registering the complaint or grievance feels heard. These are:

- **Active listening.** Focus on what is being said and, when possible, limit other distractions. If helpful or needed, take notes and make sure that the person voicing a concern agrees with the content of your notes before proceeding.

- **Empathy.** It is important to put yourself in the place of the person registering the complaint or grievance. Ask yourself how you would like the same situation handled if it were to happen to you.

- **Non-verbal communication.** Often it is not what staff members say as much as how they act—sometimes unconsciously—that can make the difference between satisfaction and dissatisfaction. Posture, expressions, and gestures can speak volumes to the person who is on the receiving end.

- **Creating rapport.** It is important that care recipients and their representatives experience some sort of connection with the staff in order to feel as if they are important to the members of the care team and not just another "task to be done."

- **Trust.** Perhaps the most essential element when dealing with patients and their representatives, but especially when handling complaints and/or grievances, is to gain their trust. This means, first and foremost, following through on anything that is promised and keeping the person informed on the progress being made at reasonable intervals.

## Drivers for Managing the Grievance and Complaint Process

The Centers for Medicare and Medicaid (CMS) develop Conditions of Participation (CoPs) and Conditions for Coverage (CfCs) which healthcare organizations must meet in order to begin and continue participating in the Medicare and Medicaid programs.[3] These health and safety standards are part of the foundation for improving quality and protecting the health and safety of beneficiaries. CMS also ensures that the standards of accrediting organizations recognized by CMS (through a process called "deeming") meet or exceed the Medicare standards set forth in the CoPs /CfCs. A Quality Improvement Organization (QIO) is a CMS contractor responsible for reviewing the appropriateness and quality of care and utilization decisions for Medicare patients in hospitals. Medicare patients may contact the QIO to lodge complaints about care quality.

As written, the CoPs for Patient Rights are an important reference for organizations as they manage the grievance process. The CoPs for Patient Rights were revised in 2005 and the final rule was issued on December 8, 2006. The effective date was October 17, 2008.[4]

The final rule contained instructions for a formal process for healthcare consumers (patients) to bring their concerns to the attention of the organization. That process includes guidance for creating a due process for hearing and resolving grievances. The guidelines explain that patients should have reasonable expectations of care and services and the facility should address those expectations in a timely, reasonable, and consistent manner. Furthermore, the CoPs require that all patients treated in an acute care setting under the Medicare program have certain protections. These requirements are codified in the United States Code of Federal Regulations, commonly referred to as CFR Section 482.13.[5]

Patient Rights is the key section describing the responsibilities of organizations to ensure the rights of patients during the care experience. CFR Section 482.13— Conditions of Participation Patient Rights—states that, "a hospital must protect and promote each patient's rights."[3] To read the entire section, refer to the Electronic Code of Federal Regulations (e-CFR) at http://ecfr.gpoaccess.gov.[6]

Simply stated, the CMS regulation specifies that the hospital must inform the patient and/or the patient's representative of the internal grievance process, including whom to contact to file a grievance. As part of its notification of patient rights, the hospital must provide the patient or the patient's representative a phone number and address for lodging a grievance with the state agency. The hospital must inform the patient that he/she may lodge a grievance with the state agency (the state agency that has licensure survey responsibility for the hospital) directly, regardless of whether he/she has first used the hospital's grievance process.

## Defining the Complaint/Grievance Process

Interpretive guidelines[7] are published by CMS to help hospitals interpret the actual meaning of the standards. Interpretive guidelines from 2011 clarified the common definitions for complaints and grievances as follows:

- A **complaint** is a concern voiced by a patient, or patient's representative, about service, care, or treatment that can be resolved quickly by the staff present. A complaint is considered resolved when the patient is satisfied with the actions taken on his or her behalf.

- A **grievance** is a written or verbal complaint by a patient, or patient's representative, about the patient's care. When a verbal complaint by the patient is not resolved at the time of the complaint by staff present, it automatically becomes a grievance.

Sometimes, situations will arise that make it difficult to determine if a concern should be classified as a complaint or a grievance. When in doubt, the recognized best practice is to classify the concern as a grievance, and respond accordingly.

| Grievance | Complaint |
|---|---|
| An issue of abuse, neglect, patient harm, or hospital compliance with CMS Conditions of Participation | An issue that is resolved promptly at the time by staff present |
| A concern related to hospital's compliance with CMS conditions of participation | A billing question (except when related to Medicare beneficiary billing) |
| A concern that is postponed or referred to another staff for later resolution | A short comment in a patient survey that would have been handled at the time, if known about |
| An issue that requires investigation or further action for resolution | |
| A written complaint (including e-mail, fax, or a comment attached to a survey) | |
| The patient or their representative requests that the concern be formally handled | |

**Staff present** is defined as any hospital staff present or close to the patient's location at the time of the complaint, who can resolve the patient's complaint promptly. Staff present may include nursing, administration, supervisors, Patient Advocates or volunteers.

 **Know the difference between a complaint and a grievance and the requirements for responding to each. Use the scenarios illustrated here and the flow chart found in this guide to help you, if needed.**

# III. Scenarios/Examples of Complaints and Grievances

## A. Complaint, regarding meals, solved at the time

Martha, age 59, is a patient in the Medical/Surgical unit of a local acute care hospital. She is recovering from cardiac surgery. She is on a restricted diet, so is already dissatisfied with her meal choices. For the past three meals, the water for her herbal tea has arrived lukewarm, and Martha likes her tea hot. She mentions this to a member of the dietary team who is picking up menus from the room. This person assures Martha that she will address her concern, and mentions it to the Assistant Director of Dietary, who relates this to the line staff. From that time onward, Martha's tea water is hot when she receives it.

## B. Complaint, regarding lost items, solved at the time

Pauline, age 70, is a patient who states that her dentures were left on her overbed table when she finished her lunch and are now missing. She calls the nurse and complains that someone must have taken them. The nurse looks around the room and not seeing the dentures, calls upon the Patient Advocate to follow up. The Patient Advocate, after hearing Pauline's story, walks down to the kitchen, where the trays from the unit have been brought, but not yet unloaded. She quickly finds the tray from Pauline's room, and sure enough, the dentures are there. She brings them back to the unit, secures a denture cup, and reminds Pauline to use the cup whenever she removes the dentures to clean her mouth. Pauline is thankful for the Advocate's efforts and promises to use the denture cup in the future.

## C. Grievance due to serious nature of allegation (e.g., abuse, neglect)

Robert, age 85, is a resident with Parkinson's at a Skilled Nursing Facility whose activities of daily living have been decreasing as his disease advances. Sometimes Robert becomes impulsive and gets out of his bed at the Skilled Nursing Facility and tries walking out to the nurses' station to ask for the daily newspaper. One evening the staff was very busy, as another resident was going into cardiac arrest, when Robert appeared at the station. A male aide yelled at Robert, "If you don't get back into that bed I'm going to tie you to that bed!" Robert's daughter was just arriving at that time and heard the interaction and phoned the Care Manager to report the verbal abuse she overheard.

## D. Grievance due to needing more time to investigate

Nancy, age 63, was admitted to the Emergency Department with chest pain. When the paramedics came to take her to the hospital, she took her purse so that she would have her medical cards and a list of her medications with her. Since her admission through the Emergency Department, she had been in the Cardiac Care

Unit, and is now in a regular patient room on the 4th floor. Once stable and in her own patient room Nancy could not find her belongings. She told the nurse, "I think the housekeeper took my purse when I was out of my room for a test." The nurse asked her why she felt this was the case, and Nancy said, "I saw her looking at it when she was here in my room yesterday cleaning." Clara, the housekeeper who takes care of the room, left yesterday to travel across country to see her new grandson, who was born the day before, and has no cell phone number on file. She is scheduled to return to work a week from tomorrow.

### E. Grievance due to letter after discharge

Henry, age 72, was recently hospitalized for six days for removal of a tumor on his left lung. His surgeon removed the tumor and sent the tissue to the lab, where it was discovered that it was malignant. An oncologist was consulted and visited Henry twice during his stay, outlining a suggested course of treatment. The pulmonologist also was consulted and Henry began pulmonary therapy, including oxygen at home. Finally, Henry's family doctor saw him three separate times during the hospitalization. Henry's wife tried to get information from the various team members, but each one suggested she speak with someone else. After Henry was discharged, she wrote an angry letter to the hospital claiming lack of communication with her and her husband and requested that the hospital reply to her grievance in a formal letter.

### F. Grievance due to letter attached to a survey requesting formal review

Myra, age 36, was hospitalized in a local psychiatric hospital for the third time in 14 months following severe bouts of depression. Each time she was admitted, a different psychiatrist reviewed her medication, and then added new medications. Although Myra is now less depressed, the amount of medication she is now taking has made her unable to work, take care of her seven-year old son, or maintain any quality of life. In addition, the cost of the medications has caused a financial hardship for the family. Repeated calls to her psychiatrist, who is the Medical Director, have gone unanswered, so Myra's husband wrote a letter to the hospital Patient Advocate, attached to the satisfaction survey, requesting a formal review of her case. In it he asked for information about consultations between the prescribing psychiatrists, and why they decided to keep her on so many different medications post-discharge.

By referring to the sample flow chart in this guide, readers can see what steps need to be taken to make sure that the complaint/grievance is solved within the allotted time and that all parties are satisfied with the process.

# IV. Sample Patient Complaint/Grievance

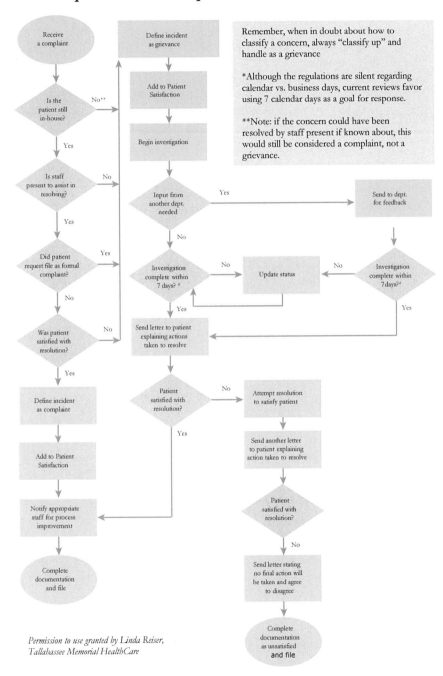

Receive a complaint

Define incident as grievance

Remember, when in doubt about how to classify a concern, always "classify up" and handle as a grievance

Add to Patient Satisfaction

Is the patient still in-house? — No** →

*Although the regulations are silent regarding calendar vs. business days, current reviews favor using 7 calendar days as a goal for response.

Yes

Begin investigation

**Note: if the concern could have been resolved by staff present if known about, this would still be considered a complaint, not a grievance.

Is staff present to assist in resolving? — No →

Input from another dept. needed — Yes → Send to dept. for feedback

Yes

No

Did patient request file as formal complaint? — Yes →

Investigation complete within 7 days? * — No → Update status ← No — Investigation complete within 7 days? *

No

Yes

Yes

Was patient satisfied with resolution? — No →

Send letter to patient explaining actions taken to resolve

Yes

Define incident as complaint

Patient satisfied with resolution? — No → Attempt resolution to satisfy patient

Yes

Add to Patient Satisfaction

Send another letter to patient explaining action taken to resolve

Notify appropriate staff for process improvement ←

Patient satisfied with resolution?

No

Complete documentation and file

Send letter stating no final action will be taken and agree to disagree

Complete documentation as unsatisfied and file

*Permission to use granted by Linda Reiser, Tallahassee Memorial HealthCare*

# V. Handling Complaints and Grievances in the Digital World

In this age of social media, patients often contact healthcare organizations to express complaints and grievances via Facebook, Twitter, Yelp, the organization's website, blogs and a variety of other methods. Organizations have to remember that the way in which they respond to these is viewed publicly and by many. This topic has generated substantial discussion on The Beryl Institute Patient Advocacy Community listserv.[2] Some of the participants shared copies of their hospital policies, which indicated that responses to complaints fielded via social media sources may only be responded to by the Public Relations department.

The following insights are provided as suggestions on how to handle complaints described here.

**Policy:** Have a policy stating that responses to complaints from this source fall into the hands of one department. The policy informs employees that there must be clearance by that department before any response is made, and rarely, if ever, should the response be over a public media source. (Usually, the Public Relations department is in control of setting the policy.)

**Response:** Complaints on social media cannot be publicly ignored. Public responses should be positive, with the promise that the complaint will be addressed personally in a private way. The organization can publicly thank the complainant, say that the feedback is appreciated, and that the concern will be followed up personally. Only specified personnel should be allowed to respond on sites such as Facebook, Yelp and the like. How the complaint is handled then is determined by the policy on complaints and grievances. It should be as if the complaint was received by more traditional methods, such as phone calls or letters.

Here is an example of a response:

> *"Your organization's name" is delighted to receive your comments. Our patients, their families, and loved ones play a large role in the perception of our hospital and we always encourage feedback. We make every effort to address compliments and concerns, and look forward to acknowledging yours. To ensure your privacy, we have created a form to help us begin direct conversation with you via email or phone. Please use this form to give us your preferred method of private communication: <link to your organization's form>".*

CoPs and The Joint Commission say that a complaint received by e-mail may be responded to by e-mail. Any PHI (Personal Health Information) must be handled in a HIPAA compliant manner. That type of correspondence is personal and private and is not to be responded to in a way that can be viewed publicly. The policy must be clear that there are strict consequences for replying publicly to a social media comment or complaint without permission.

# VI. Regulatory Protection for Patients

## State Based Protections for Patients

Not all guidance comes from the Federal government. It is important to also be aware of state requirements. The more stringent standards (state or Federal) apply for survey purposes. Check with your state Department of Health, state hospital association or state medical association for guidance.

## Accreditation from Various Organizations

Many healthcare organizations seek accreditation from various organizations. As The Joint Commission (TJC) is one of the commonly sought after accrediting bodies, we will highlight their regulations:

A Joint Commission standard, RI.01.01.10,[9] speaks to the Rights and Responsibilities of the Individual. This standard dictates that the hospital respects, protects, and promotes patient rights in the following ways:

- Has a written policy on patient rights
- Informs the patient of his/her rights
- Treats the patient in a dignified and respectful manner that supports his/her dignity
- Respects the patient's right to and need for effective communication
- Respects the patient's cultural and personal values, beliefs, and preferences
- Respects the patient's right to privacy
- Right to voice complaints without reprisal (RI.01.07.01[9])
- Respects the patient's right to pain management
- Accommodates the patient's right to religious and other spiritual services
- Allows the patient to access, request amendment to, and obtain information on disclosures of his or her health information, in accordance with law and regulation
- Allows a family member, friend, or other individual to be present with the patient for emotional support during the course of the stay
- Prohibits discrimination based on age, race, ethnicity, religion, culture, language, physical or mental disability, socioeconomic status, gender, sexual orientation, and gender identity or expression

Standard RI.02.01.01[9] states that the hospital shall inform the patient about his/her responsibilities related to their own care, treatment, and services. It states that the hospital has a written policy that defines patient responsibilities, including but not limited to:

* Providing information that facilitates his/her care, treatment, and services

* Asking questions or acknowledging when the patient does not understand the treatment course or care decision

* Following instructions, policies, rules, and regulations in place to support quality
  care for all patients and a safe environment for all individuals in the hospital

* Supporting mutual consideration and respect by maintaining civil language and conduct in interactions with staff and licensed independent practitioners

* Meeting financial commitments

Informing the patient about his/her responsibilities can be shared verbally, in writing, or both.

The Joint Commission, in its work to enforce the COPs, has also created a Standard that applies to organizations. Standard RI.01.07.01[9] states that patients and their families or representatives have the right to have complaints reviewed by the hospital. The standard established a complaint resolution process that does the following:

* Informs the patient and his or her family/representative about the complaint resolution process

* Reviews and, when possible, resolves the complaints from the patient and his or her family/representative

* Acknowledges receipt of a complaint that the hospital cannot resolve immediately and notifies the patient of follow-up to the complaint

* Provides the patient and his or her family/representative with the phone number and address needed to file a complaint with the relevant state authority

* Allows the patient and his or her family/representative to voice complaints and recommend changes freely without being subject to coercion, discrimination, reprisal, or unreasonable interruption of care

* Provides the individual with a written notice of its decision that contains the name of the hospital contact person, the steps taken on behalf of the individual to investigate the complaint, the results of the process, and the date of completion of the complaint process

# VII. Grievance Procedures and Timelines

The grievance process must specify time frames for review of the grievance and the provision of a response. The hospital must review, investigate, and resolve each patient's grievance within a reasonable time frame. For example, grievances about situations that endanger the patient, such as neglect or abuse, should be reviewed immediately, given the seriousness of the allegations and the potential for harm to the patient(s). Regardless of the nature of the grievance, the hospital should make sure that it is responding to the substance of each grievance while identifying, investigating, and resolving any deeper, systemic problems indicated by the grievance. Occasionally a grievance is complicated and may require an extensive investigation.

The CMS Interpretive Guidelines (issued in 2005) provide the following regarding timeframes:

*We recognize that staff scheduling as well as fluctuations in the numbers and complexity of grievances can affect the timeframes for the provision of written responses.*

*On average, a timeframe of seven days for the provision of the response would be considered appropriate. We do not require that every grievance be resolved during the specified timeframe although most should be resolved. The Code of Federal Regulations at 42 CFR §482.13(a)(2)(iii) specifies information the hospital must include in their response.*

*If the grievance will not be resolved, or if the investigation is not or will not be completed within seven days\*, the hospital should inform the patient or the patient's representative that the hospital is still working to resolve the grievance and that the hospital will follow-up with a written response within a stated number of days in accordance with each hospital's grievance policy. The hospital must attempt to resolve all grievances as soon as possible.*[8]

**Consider including the following in your organization's grievance policy:**
**What time frames are established to review and respond to patient grievances?**

• **Are these time frames clearly explained in the organization's grievance policy that is shared with patients?**

\*Although the regulations are silent regarding calendar vs. business days, current reviews favor using seven calendar days as a goal for response.

## Establishing a Grievance Committee

An integral part of the responsibilities of the organization is ensuring participation in the handling of grievances by a Grievance Committee. Failure to respond appropriately and in a timely manner has critical implications for your organization.

## The Role of Governance

The hospital's governing body must approve and be responsible for the effective operation of the grievance process, and must review and resolve grievances, unless it delegates the responsibility, in writing, to a Grievance Committee. According to the CMS Interpretive Guidelines §482.13(a)(2)[7]:

*The hospital's governing body is responsible for the effective operation of the grievance process, which includes the hospital's compliance with all the CMS grievance process requirements. The hospital's governing body must review and resolve grievances, unless it delegates this responsibility in writing to a Grievance Committee. A committee is more than one person. The committee membership must have adequate numbers of qualified members to review and resolve the grievances the hospital receives (this includes providing written responses) in a manner that complies with the CMS grievance process requirements.*

## Grievance Committee Members and Roles

- The Grievance Committee, as designated by the hospital's Board of Directors, is responsible for the effective operation of the grievance process.
- The Grievance Committee shall have at least two or more members.
- Depending on your hospital's policy, the process of the grievance resolution includes tracking, investigating, and responding (see flow sheet).
- It is expected that grievances reported will be used to implement improvements.
- Patient Advocates or any person in the facility reporting grievances will present grievances to the hospital Grievance Committee according to the grievance policy (following the timeframe in your policy).
- Members of the Grievance Committee could include:
  - Risk Manager for possible litigation cases;
  - Quality and Safety Director to evaluate process improvements;
  - Executive Medical Director for physician concerns;
  - Chief Nursing Officer for nursing concerns;
  - Patient Financial Services Manager for possible charge audits or charge adjustments.
- The Grievance Committee may refer grievances to appropriate hospital committees for review including but not limited to Medical Staff Performance Review Committee, Ethics Committee, or Utilization Review

To assess evidence of compliance with the CoPs, use the following statements to assess your level of readiness regarding a Grievance Committee:

- The hospital has a process in place to address complaints/grievances
- The hospital's governing body is responsible for reviewing and resolving grievances

— or —

- Has delegated responsibility in writing to a Grievance Committee
- Has approved the grievance process in place and has demonstrated this approval in writing
- Assumes ultimate responsibility that the grievance process is effective, and is reviewed and analyzed through the hospital's QA/ PI process or other mechanism that provides oversight of the grievance process

## Organizing for an Effective Grievance Process

As you consider how to meet the intent of the CoPs and The Joint Commission standards, it is helpful to understand the roles and responsibilities of the Grievance Committee. Included here is an overview and flow chart for organizing for an effective grievance process.

Essential Components of the Grievance Process[10]

- The Hospital's governing body is responsible for the grievance process unless delegated to the Grievance Committee. This must be documented in writing.

- The Grievance Committee must effectively initiate the grievance process and present findings to Quality Improvement to identify opportunities for improvement.

- The Grievance Committee must ensure that the grievance process is reviewed and analyzed by Quality Improvement for effectiveness.

# Sample Grievance Process Flow Chart

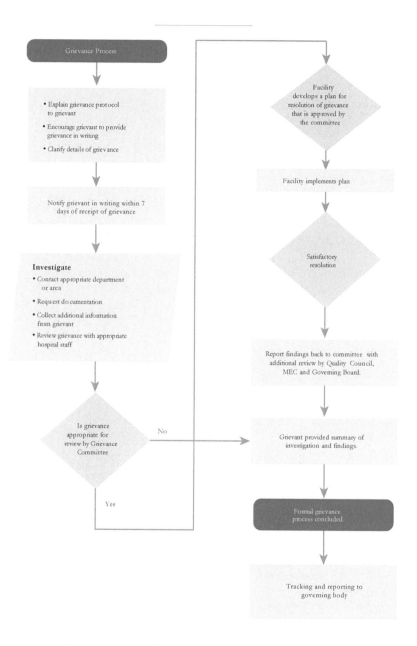

**Grievance Process**

- Explain grievance protocol to grievant
- Encourage grievant to provide grievance in writing
- Clarify details of grievance

Notify grievant in writing within 7 days of receipt of grievance

**Investigate**
- Contact appropriate department or area
- Request documentation
- Collect additional information from grievant
- Review grievance with appropriate hospital staff

Is grievance appropriate for review by Grievance Committee

No

Yes

Facility develops a plan for resolution of grievance that is approved by the committee

Facility implements plan

Satisfactory resolution

Report findings back to committee with additional review by Quality Council, MEC and Governing Board.

Grievant provided summary of investigation and findings.

Formal grievance process concluded.

Tracking and reporting to governing body

*Permission to use granted by Mary Willis, Desert Regional Medical Center*

## Preparing a Grievance Policy and Establishing a Procedure

To achieve compliance with the CMS standards, develop a policy that outlines the process that meets both the intent of the requirements and the needs of your organization.

The following steps should assist you. Also refer to The Beryl Institute Patient Advocacy Community list serv[2] and website for additional resources.

Read and be familiar with CMS 482.13 Conditions of Participation, Patient Rights Section. Understand the difference between a policy and procedure.

- Policies are guiding principles put in place that give direction as to what needs to be done and why it needs to be done
  - Policies control the actions, activities, and conduct of the people and systems in the organization
  - Policies let the reader know the organization's stand on a matter and why there must be a rule about it
  - Policies also help the organization avoid violating regulations and laws
  - The complaint management and grievance process policy should always be an administrative policy–meaning that it applies throughout the organization. It is required that the governing body approve the policy.

- Procedures are the "how" or the way of handling things
  - They provide step-by-step instructions, or actions to achieve the task/goal
  - They complement the policies and are action oriented

Start with a draft. Get input and discuss it with leadership. Included in this guide is a template that can be used to develop a grievance policy. Most organizations have standard formats for all policies. This template is provided to ensure that all required elements of the standards are included in your policy.

## Essential Components of Grievance Policy

- Ensure that patients and/or their representatives have the information necessary to exercise their rights, both inpatient and outpatient

- Create a grievance process that encourages all personnel to alert appropriate staff concerning any patient grievance

- Verify that the hospital's policy provides for determining when a patient has a representative and who that patient's representative is, consistent with this guidance and state law
  - Must facilitate an expeditious and non-discriminatory resolution of disputes where an individual is the patient's representative

- Must address HIPPA regulations. Should clearly designate a consent process for release of private health information (PHI) in the event that the complainant is not the patient.
- Establish a process/procedure for prompt resolution
- Establish who will oversee the grievance policy—the governing body or grievance committee. A grievance committee is defined as more than one person.
- Include a mechanism for timely referral of Medicare patient concerns to the Quality Improvement Organization. Establish time frames or reference Medicare complaint policy
- Address oversight of compliance with grievance policy

## Essential Components of Grievance Procedure

- Must establish a clearly explained procedure for the submission of a patient's written or verbal grievance to the hospital. This means the patient or patient's representative should be able to clearly understand the procedure and clearly know how to submit either a verbal or a written grievance
- The hospital must respond to the grievance made by the patient or patient's representative by written response via letter (or e-mail dependent on whether the hospital has a policy against the communication to patient via email) and provide the following:
  - Name of the hospital
  - Contact person
  - Steps taken on behalf of the patient to investigate the grievance – Results of the grievance
  - Date of completion
- The process must specify time frames for review of the grievance and the provision of a response
  - On average, a time frame of seven calendar days for the provision of response is appropriate
  - If the grievance is not resolved, or if the investigation is not or will not be completed within seven days, you must inform the patient or patient's representative that the hospital is still working to resolve the grievance and that the hospital will follow-up with the patient or patient's representative in a stated number of days

- A grievance is considered resolved when:
  - The patient is satisfied with the actions taken on their behalf
  - The hospital has taken appropriate and reasonable actions to resolve the grievance, but the patient or patient's representative remains unsatisfied with the hospital's actions. If this occurs, the hospital may consider the grievance closed and must maintain documentation of its efforts and demonstrate compliance with CMS requirements.

Regulatory agencies spend a lot of time developing the requirements and interpretive guidelines. When they visit your organization and review policies, they like to see that you cite these as references.

Templates and examples of letters can be found in "The Written Word" available on The Beryl Institute website[2].

# Sample Grievance Policy

| | |
|---|---|
| **Department** | Department where your policy originates. |
| **Policy #:** | Number assigned for quick and easy reference |
| **Page:** | All pages of policy should include current page and total pages (i.e. 3 of 5) |
| **Effective Date:** | Date policy becomes effective and generally, date the review process has been completed and policy is ready to be published. |
| **Approved By:** | Department where your policy originates. |

| | |
|---|---|
| **Purpose:** | A concise description for the reason of implementation of the policy. |
| **Scope:** | A list of departments or job titles affected by or required to comply with the policy |
| **Policy:** | A general description of the action to be taken in order to obtain the desired outcome or goal of the policy |

**RELEVANT FACTORS:**

| | |
|---|---|
| **Definitions:** | A list of clear defined terms used in the policy for easy comprehension by the reader of the policy. (This would include but is not limited to: Patient and/or Patient Representative, Complaint, Grievance, etc.) |
| **Procedures:** | List of required steps taken in order to achieve compliance of stated policy. |
| **Precautions:** | List of any particular conditions to which the reader should be aware of in implementing the stated policy. |
| **Supportive Data:** | List of supporting evidence to promote and emphasize significance of policy. |
| | Note: If a relevant factor is not applicable, list Not Applicable. |

| | |
|---|---|
| **Policy Owner:** | Name of person or committee where policy originated and who is responsible for updating and maintaining policy. |
| **References:** | List reference, resources, standards used in development of policy. |
| **Related Documents:** | List other documents, policies or procedures that are relevant to the application of this policy. (i.e. Patient Rights, The Joint Commission Standards, etc.). |
| **Origination Date:** | Date policy is put into effect. |
| **Revision Dates:** | First revision date of the policy and any hereafter. |
| **Last Review Date:** | Date policy was last reviewed. |
| **Next Review Date:** | Date set forth by the Policy Owner for a regulated review of policy. Policy Owner should determine time span between reviews. |
| **Date Retired:** | Date policy is no longer in effect. |

*Permission to use granted by Jessica Chambers, East Tennessee Children's Hospital*

## VIII. Requirement to Incorporate Grievance Data into Your Hospital's Quality Program

When CMS or state surveyors visit your facility, they are looking for "meaningful" data. They not only want to see what you are doing, but the how's and why's of your program. They want to see evidence that your organization is using your program to make things better for patients. Working with your Quality Department, and others as appropriate, your efforts will be visible. Demonstrate your focus on quality and patient experience in the following ways:

• Use the central theme of your grievances to create your performance improvement objectives. For instance, if you see the trend of poor communication by the ED staff coming across in your grievances, perhaps you can work with the ED staff management to educate, track, and quantify the improvement in this area.

• Many organizations have a Patient Safety and/or Adverse Health Events Committee. Bring your grievances to this committee for review. Perhaps a common thread exists between what the patients and their families are telling you and what the hospital's incident reporting system is saying. By partnering with others, you will be affecting the overall quality assurance process.

# IX. Service Recovery Approach

Service recovery is the process used to acknowledge dissatisfaction of patients, or their families, by identifying or resolving problems, or making amends for a failure in customer or clinical service. Usually, hospital staff are empowered to provide service recovery at the time a service excellence shortfall is identified. An apology to patients about their experience or inconvenience can go a long way if acted upon immediately by staff.

If a patient or family remains dissatisfied, refer them to the Patient Advocate (give phone number) or contact the Patient Advocate on their behalf.

Work collaboratively with key stakeholders when establishing your Service Recovery program. Be sure to discuss the process with your Risk Management team so that you can present guidelines collaboratively on when Service Recovery should be used and when the issue should be escalated to your Risk Management team.

An effective Service Recovery plan:

* Empowers employees to take quick and decisive action when something has gone wrong

* Creates a base of radically loyal customers who provide valuable word-of-mouth advertising

* Prevents the negative word-of-mouth advertising that inevitably comes from a dissatisfied customer

* Is a vital part of any organization that is serious about offering superior service

* Is used to identify and upgrade customer service opportunities on an ongoing basis

* Is used to identify and correct problems before a customer encounters them and to upgrade the service before the patient is discharged

- Is a vital communication tool for listening to the customer and observing for signs of dissatisfaction

- Improves the overall patient experience by showing that every member of the team is invested in meeting the patient's needs

 Effective use of service recovery might prevent a complaint from becoming a grievance.

## Sample Service Recovery Model: A-C-T

**A – Apologize** (Acknowledge the customer's concern)
**C – Correct** (Take action—fix the problem and do something extra to make amends)
**T – Trend** (Track service failures and learn from them to improve services)

| More Effective | Less Effective |
|---|---|
| Let me see what I can do for you | You're right – the service is disgraceful |
| I'm sorry that we did not meet your expectations | I can't believe that happened to you |
| I am so sorry for the inconvenience | Call Customer Service |
| Let me fix that. How may I make this better for you? | I don't have the time right now |
| This is not my expertise, but I can assist you | Just calm down |
| I can assist you with solving your concern | It's not my fault |
| Thank you for letting me know. I will let the department know | It's no big deal |
| I fully understand. How may I help you? | This is what you need to do... |
| Let me research this and I will follow-up with you in (specific time) | I'm sorry if... |
| Let me see what I can do for you | I'm sorry, but |
| I'm sorry that we did not meet your expectations | I can't do anything about that |
| I am so sorry for the inconvenience | That's not my department |
| Thank you for bringing this to my attention | We know that's a problem |
| You are right. Let me help you | That's our policy, there's nothing I can do |
| I see your point. This is how I can help... | No, that's not true |

Sample Service Recovery Tools

- A gift shop certificate
- A free meal or snack in the cafeteria
- A fruit basket
- A bouquet of flowers
- A visit from a manager or administrator
- A replacement for a lost item
- A handwritten apology
- A stuffed animal
- A company t-shirt
- A creative gift matched to a specific situation

 **Patient Advocates are encouraged to play an active role in creating and presenting a service recovery model so that employees are empowered to effectively engage in the process.**

Suggestions for implementing and sustaining a service recovery program include:

- Begin with your hospital leaders. Leaders must model the behaviors you are seeking to facilitate a successful program
- Introduce the model during new employee orientation
- Present the model and train staff during departmental meetings
- Create a brochure promoting the model
- Attach the model to your hospital's complaint policy
- Create a link on your hospital's internal intranet website or communication board
- Create a service recovery toolkit

Do's and Don'ts of Service Recovery

| Do | Don't |
|---|---|
| Ensure the item matches the infraction. The item given should directly address the service variance which occurred | Give a service recovery item for a serious infraction such as a medical error without consultation |
| Fix the issue first if possible. Service recovery items should never replace righting a wrong. | Use a service recovery without fixing (or explaining the reason you are unable to fix) the situation first |
| Encourage the items to be provided by the team member closest to the issue | Use the items as a way to avoid a personal and direct apology |
| Identify the root cause of the variance and fix the core issue so it doesn't impact other patients | Use service recovery items for non-service related issues. Establish a separate process for hardship and charity |
| Round on the patient frequently following a service variance | End the encounter after giving a service recovery item, continued contact is important. |

## Limits on Gift Giving and Service Recovery Guidelines from OIG

Most hospital compliance plans include limitations on service recovery to no more than $10 per item, or $50 in aggregate on an annual basis. This is a guideline in place as part of the anti-inducement law for Medicare and Medicaid patients[14,15].

In 2010, the Patient Protection and Affordable Care Act[13] added some new exceptions to the original law, including a new exception for rewards offered by retailers that meet the following criteria:

• The rewards could consist of coupons, rebates, or other rewards from a retailer

• The rewards must be offered to the general public, regardless of health insurance status

• The offer of rewards cannot be tied to the provision of other items or services reimbursed in whole or in part by the Medicare or Medicaid programs

 **Be sure your service recovery policy takes these limits and exceptions into account and that you inform staff of the limits.**

# Sample Service Recovery Flow Chart

*Patient Service Officer or Patient Advocate

*Permission to use granted by Mohammed Jassim FACHE,SHRM,HIA,ACII, Cleveland Clinic Abu*

# X. Charting Your Course

Five essential principles should guide your approach to ensure that the person registering the complaint or grievance feels heard. These include active listening, empathy, non-verbal communication, creating rapport and trust. These principles ensure that you are not only following the letter of the law, but are doing what is right for the patient, who is after all, the center of all you do.

- Know the difference between a complaint and a grievance and the requirements for responding to each. Use the scenarios and the flow chart found in this guide to help you, if needed.

- Consider including the following in your organization's grievance policy.

  – What time frames are established to review and respond to patient grievances?

  – Are these time frames clearly explained in the organization's grievance policy that is shared with patients?

- To assess evidence of compliance with the COPs, the following statements will help you assess your level of readiness regarding a grievance committee:

  – The hospital has a process in place to address complaints/grievances
  – The hospital's governing body is responsible for reviewing and resolving grievances—or—

    - Has delegated responsibility in writing to a grievance committee
    - Has approved the grievance process in place—and—has demonstrated this approval in writing
    - Assumes ultimate responsibility that the grievance process is effective, and is reviewed and analyzed through the hospital's QA/ PI process or other mechanism that provides oversight of the grievance process

- Effective use of service recovery might prevent a complaint from becoming a grievance.

- Tips for preparing a grievance policy: Before you begin writing a policy, read and be familiar with CMS 482.13 Conditions of Participation, Patient Rights Section. Understand the difference between a policy and procedure.

- Patient Advocates are encouraged to play an active role in creating and presenting a service recovery model to their respective institutions so that every employee will be empowered to effectively engage in the process.

- Be sure your service recovery policy takes the OIG limits and exceptions into account and that all involved are aware of them.

- Regulatory agencies spend a lot of time developing the requirements and interpretive guidelines. When they visit your organization and review policies, they like to see that you cite these as references.

- Templates and examples of letters can be found in "The Written Word" available on The Beryl Institute website[2].

# XI. Resources

1. CMS Manual System, Dept. of Health & Human Services (DHHS), Pub. 100-07 State Operations—Provider Certification—

   www.cms.gov

   Centers for Medicare & Medicaid Services Survey & Certification Group/ Division of Acute Care Services

   - 7500 Security Boulevard, Mailstop 02-17-26, Baltimore, MD 21244
   - Toll-Free: 1-877-267-2323 or Local: 410-786-3000

   CMS Interpretive Guidelines for complaints/grievances
   https://www.cms.gov/Medicare/Provider-Enrollment-and-Certification/SurveyCertificationGenInfo/downloads/SCLetter05-42.pdf

2. The Beryl Institute — Patient Advocacy Community (listserv) (see website)

   The Beryl Institute — Publications
   http://www.theberylinstitute.org/?page=PatientAdvResources

   - *The Written Word*. 2011 Expanded Edition: *The Written Word: Guidelines for Responding in Writing to Patient Concerns*
   - *In the Name of the Patient*, 5th edition, 2014

3. Conditions of Participation and Conditions for Coverage:
   http://www.cms.gov/Regulations-and-Guidance/Legislation/CFCsAndCoPs/ Hospitals.html

4. Centers for Medicare & Medicaid Services (CMS), Transmittal 37 – October 17, 2008

   https://www.cms.gov/transmittals/downloads/R37SOMA.pdf

5. Federal Register / Vol. 71, No. 236 / Friday, December 8, 2006 / Rules and Regulations

   http://www.gpo.gov/fdsys/pkg/FR-2006-12-08/content-detail.html http://www.gpo.gov/fdsys/pkg/FR-2006-12-08/pdf/06-9559.pdf

6. E-Code of Federal Regulation (e-CFR)
   http://www.gpo.gov/fdsys/browse/collectionCfr.action?collectionCode=CFR

7. Interpretive Guidelines§482.13(a)(2)(i)(ii)(iii) Center for Medicaid & Medicare Services website: https://www.cms.gov/Medicare/Provider-Enrollment-and-Certification/SurveyCertificationGenInfo/downloads/SCLetter05-42.pdf

8. 482.13 (a) 2 Hospital Conditions of Participation and Interpretive Guidelines for Patients Rights.

9. The Joint Commission E-dition, Hospital, February 1, 2015 The Joint Commission

   One Renaissance Boulevard Oakbrook Terrace, Illinois 60181 1-800-994-6610

   complaint@jointcommission.org

10. August 18, 2005 Memo from the Centers for Medicare & Medicaid Services on the Revisions to Interpretive Guidelines for Centers for Medicare & Medicaid Services Hospital Conditions of Participation 42 CFR §§482.12, 482.13, 482.27 and 482.28

11. State Operations Manual

    Appendix A — Survey Protocol, Regulations and Interpretive Guidelines for Hospitals

    A-0119 (Rev. 37, Issued: 10-17-08; Effective/Implementation Date: 10-17-08) 482.13(a)(2)

12. The Medicare and Medicaid Patient Protection Act of 1987, as amended, 42 U.S.C. §1320a-7b (the "Anti-kickback Statute")

13. http://dpc.senate.gov/healthreformbill/healthbill04.pdf The Patient Protection and Affordable Care Act Detailed Summary

14. https://oig.hhs.gov/fraud/docs/alertsandbulletins/SABGiftsandInducements.pdf

15. https://www.manatt.com/health-law/federal-anti-inducement-law-creates-opportunities-for-providers/

# Appendix A1

## Preparing for The Joint Commission (TJC) Survey

There is a specific complaint and grievance standard that The Joint Commission surveyors will use when surveying your organization. The standard, RI.01.07.01[9] states, "The patient and his or her family have the right to have complaints reviewed by the hospital."[1] It is helpful for you to have the most recent version of the standard and its elements of performance. The online version has the standard and a crosswalk to the CMS requirement[4], as well as information on whether the standard requires measures of success (MOS).

Your organization may have a subscription to the online or "E-dition" version of the most recent Joint Commission manual[9]. Otherwise, it is available as a yearly-updated and published manual. In it are the regulations and Elements of Performance that describe the patient's rights and responsibilities regarding complaints and grievances.

### First Things First
The surveyor will look for a policy that describes the way the hospital handles complaints. There must be clear assignment of this process to either the governing body or a grievance committee. The surveyor will look for evidence that the process is explained to the patient and/or representative. There must be reasonable timeframes stated in the policy, and there must be evidence that the hospital follows its policy. This may be in your patient information guide, your patient bill of rights, or somewhere else that is clearly seen and easily understood by patients and families. There must be information given that includes how to contact, both in writing and by phone, the state complaint authority or The Joint Commission, in addition to explaining the complaint process within the organization.

### Tracer Activity
During a tracer activity, surveyors may ask patients and families if they know how to file a grievance in order to see whether you have given the information to the patients as you state in your policy. Be prepared to show examples of the documents that have that information.

### Other Documents and Records
Surveyors will want to see examples of how the hospital records, tracks, and resolves complaints and grievances. You should be prepared to show a record of how long it takes to process and respond to a complaint, and how you keep the patient or family/representative apprised if the time frame will be longer than the stated time due to the investigative process. They will also want to see examples of your responses to grievances to see if you include the required elements. Evidence that Medicare patients are aware of how to question what they believe to be a premature discharge[7] must also be shown, if requested.

# Appendix A2

## The Beryl Institute Patient Advocacy Community Code of Ethics

Members of the Patient Advocacy Community of The Beryl Institute who serve as patient advocates are committed to conducting their professional relationship in accordance with the following principles:

- Patient advocates have a primary responsibility to the patient.
- Patient advocates are fair, objective and caring within the scope of their professional liabilities.
- Patient advocates have an obligation to inform Patients and/or their representatives of their rights and responsibilities and advocate on their behalf.
- Patient advocates promote the autonomy and dignity of each individual and act to prevent discrimination.
- Patient advocates protect and promote the confidentiality of those served and educate patients to the limits of that confidentiality.
- Patient advocates maintain the integrity of the profession by identifying, developing, and utilizing knowledge to set standards for professional practice.
- Patient advocates are committed to continuing education to maintain professional excellence.
- Patient advocates permit no exploitation of their position. They do not endorse or promote products for financial gain.

Made in the USA
San Bernardino, CA
07 September 2015